www.jackierosecomic.com

Printed in China

ISBN: 978-0-9899829-0-0

First edition November 2013

BY JOSH ULRICH

BOOK ONE
THE TREASURE OF CAPTAIN READ

DEDICATED TO MOM

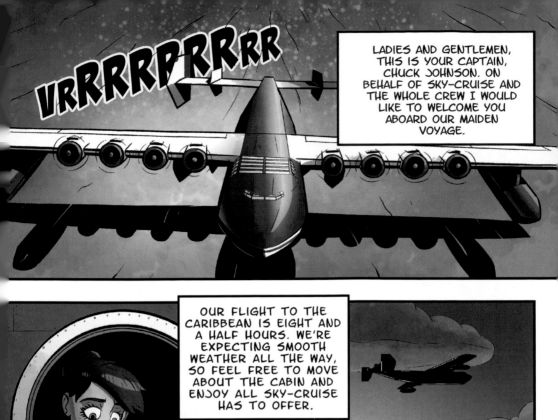

YOUR DRESS IS REALLY PRETTY.

HUH?

I SAID YOUR DRESS IS VERY PRETTY.

OH, THANK YOU.

YOUR, UH, OUTFIT IS VERY LOVELY AS WELL.

WERE YOU WAITING FOR SOMEBODY?

YES. AND THEY'RE LATE, AS USUAL.

I'M JACKIE.

DIAN.

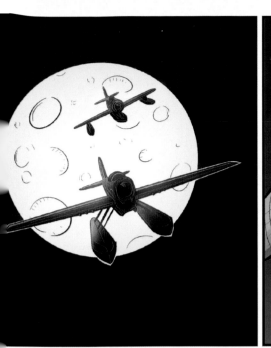

GET DOWN!

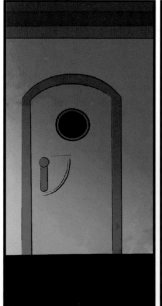

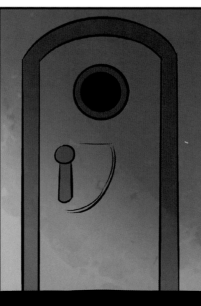

HEH...

WELL NOW. WHAT DO WE HAVE HERE?

EDDIE!

SO, WHAT ARE A BUNCH OF KIDS DOING RUNNING AROUND DOWN HERE?

DON'T YOU KNOW IT'S DANGEROUS

YOU'RE NOT GOING TO GET AWAY WITH THIS! MY DAD IS THE CAPTAIN!

YOUR DAD IS THE CAPTAIN?

EDDIE, NO.

THAT'S RIGHT

NOW IF YOU'LL EXCUSE ME, I HAVE SOME PHONE CALLS TO MAKE.

WHAT DID THEY DO WITH DIAN?

I DON'T KNOW, THEY TOOK HER TO A DIFFERENT ROOM.

-CLICK-

WE'LL HAVE TO COME BACK FOR HER, WE DON'T HAVE TIME TO LOOK FOR HER NOW.

HAVE TIME....? WHAT ARE YOU DOING?

ESCAPING, WHAT'S IT LOOK LIKE?

JACKIE, THAT'S ELIZABETH READ!

ELIZABETH READ...?

DO YOU HAVE ANY IDEA WHAT SHE WILL DO TO US IF WE'RE CAUGHT TRYING TO ESCAPE?

GUESS WE BETTER NOT STICK AROUND TO FIND OUT.

YOU WOULD THINK A WOMAN WHO LIVES ON AN AIR SHIP WOULD BE BETTER AT TYING KNOTS.

OVER HERE, THERE'S A BALCONY!

JACKIE.

ALRIGHT YOU KIDS--

NYAH!

STOP!

THROTTLE

VRRRRRRRRRR

I SAID...

LET...

BRRROOW!

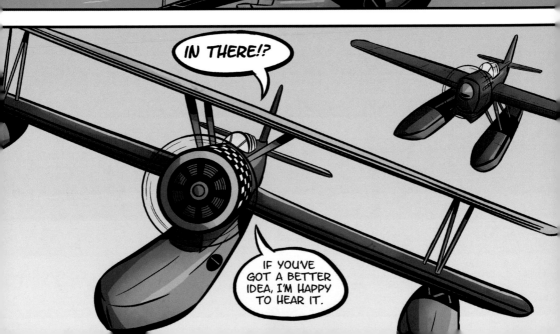

HOLD ON!

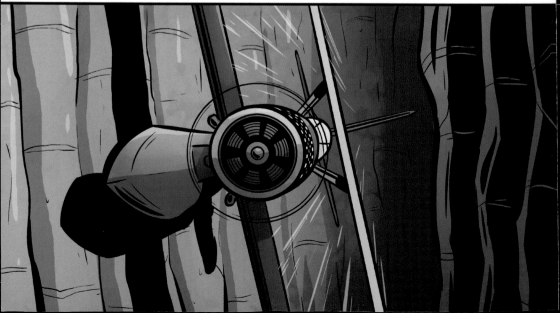

DID WE LOSE ANY?

THERE WERE THREE BEFORE, RIGHT?

RIGHT.

NO, WE DIDN'T LOSE ANY.

COME ON! THAT WAS SUPER HARD! WE SHOULD HAVE LOST **ONE** OF THEM!

WHAT SHOULD I...

...DO?

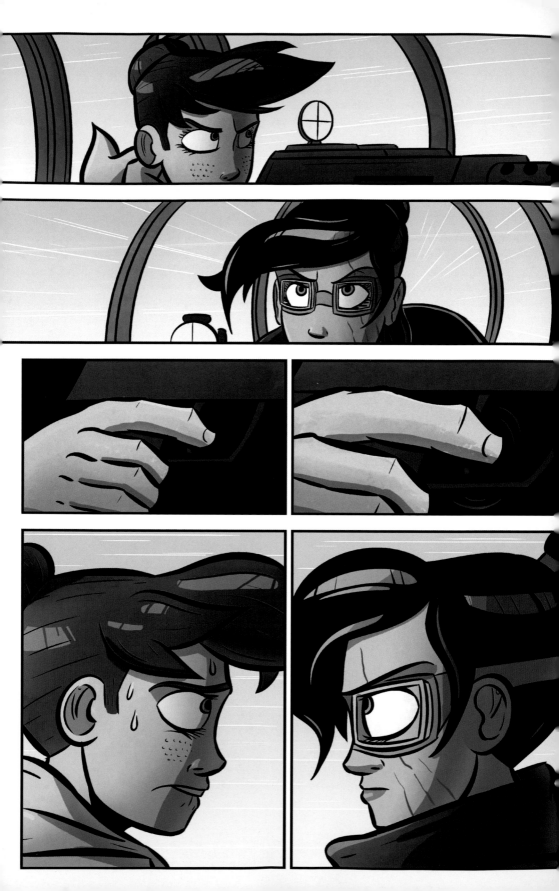

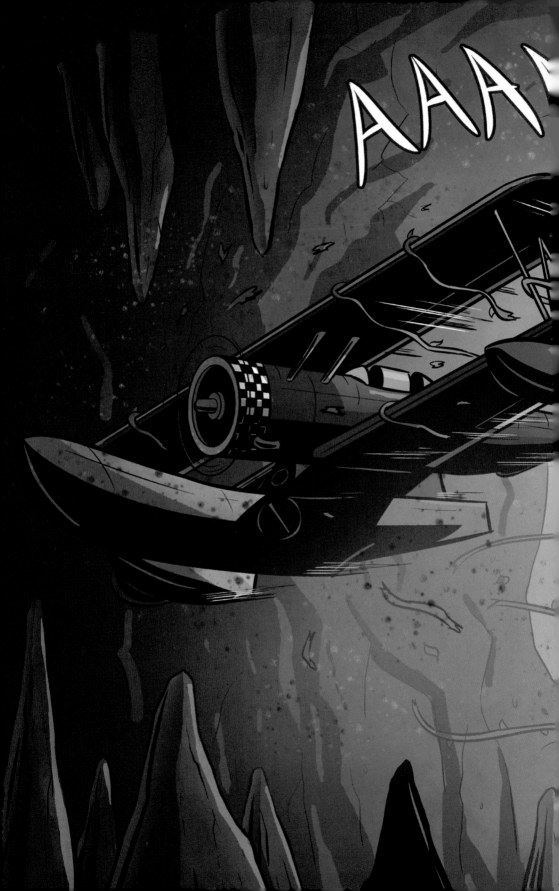

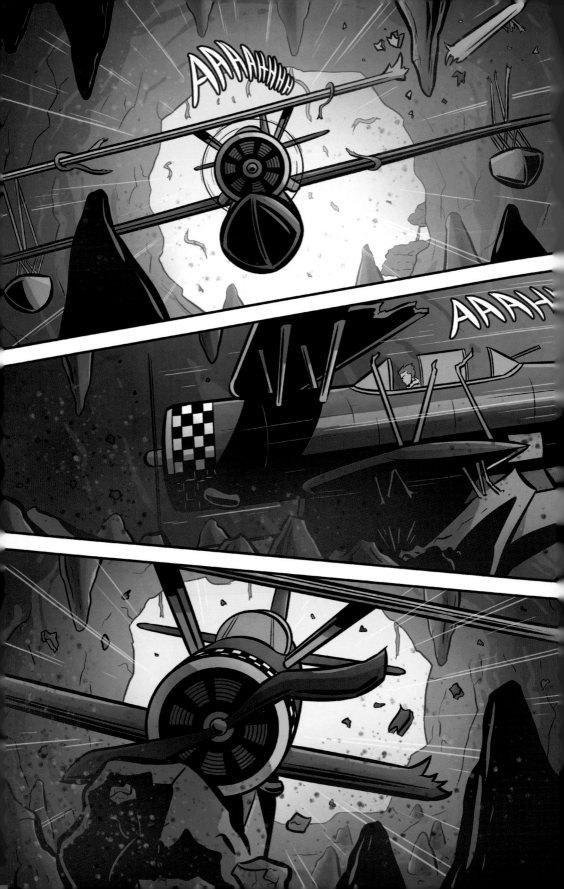

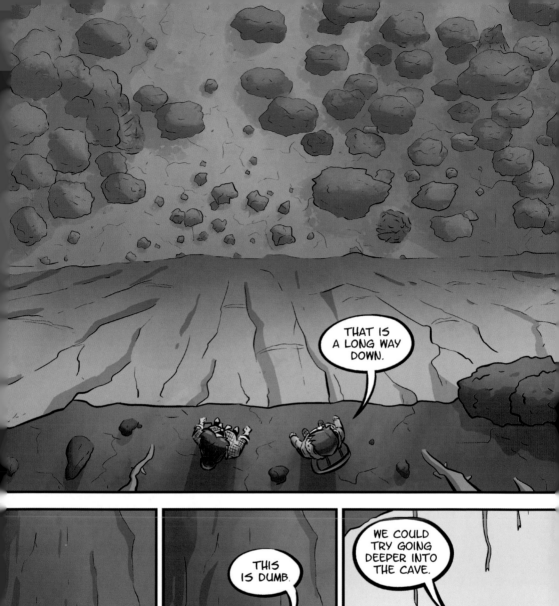

THAT IS A LONG WAY DOWN.

THIS IS DUMB.

WE COULD TRY GOING DEEPER INTO THE CAVE.

AND GET LOST FOREVER? NO THANKS.

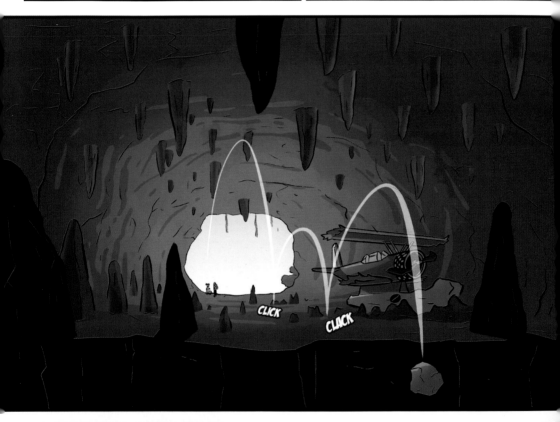

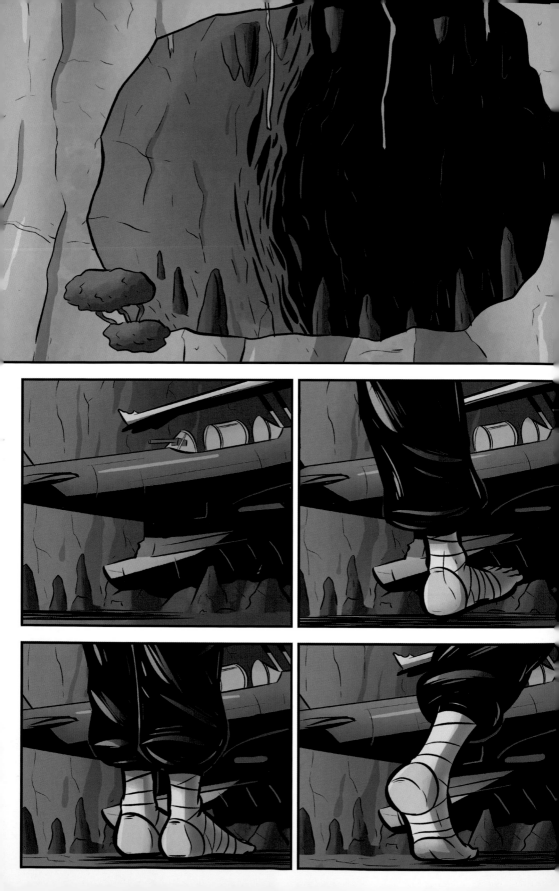

CAN I ASK YOU SOMETHING?

JACKIE, YOU CAN ASK ME **ANYTHING.**

WHAT?

NOTHING. YOU WERE SAYING?

IT'S JUST... WHAT WAS IT LIKE GROWING UP WITHOUT PARENTS? I MEAN, BEFORE YOU WERE ADOPTED.

OH.

THERE IT IS!

WHAT ARE YOU DOING? WE'VE GOT TO GET OUT OF HERE!

I'M **NOT** LEAVING WITHOUT THAT CROWN!

GIVE ME MORE SLACK!

I CAN'T! THE ROPE IS TOO SHORT!

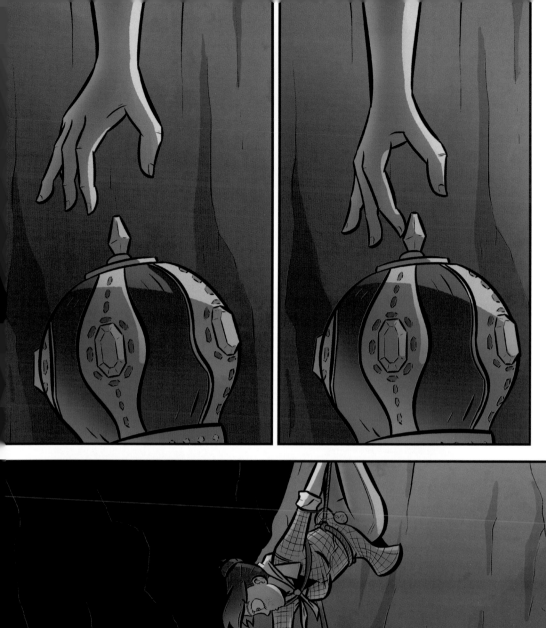

SNAP!

JACKIE! CATCH!

GASP

JACKIE! YOU'RE OKAY!

YEAH, THANKS TO DIAN.

...ABOUT THAT.

YOU...

YOU'RE ONE OF THEM?

SORRY, JACKIE. I'M AFRAID YOU HAVE TO COME WITH US.

AN INTERESTING ONE, THIS ELIZABETH READ.

SIR?

MULTIPLE CASES OF GRAND THEFT, THOUGH NO CHARGES OF MURDER OR KIDNAPPING.

WHAT'S YOUR POINT SIR?

WHAT IS A JEWEL THIEF DOING KIDNAPPING A COUPLE KIDS? IT DOESN'T FIT HER PROFILE.

WITH RESPECT, CAPTAIN HUXLEY, WHAT DIFFERENCE DOES IT MAKE? A PIRATE IS A PIRATE.

KNOWING WHAT DRIVES YOUR ENEMY IS EVERYTHING, LIEUTENANT. READ HAS EITHER BECOME DESPERATE, OR THERE IS SOMETHING MORE AT WORK HERE.

WE MUST PROCEED WITH CAUTION UNTIL WE KNOW WHAT'S REALLY GOING ON.

I DON'T KNOW WHAT I'M GOING TO DO, SHEPHERD.

YOU SHOULD HAVE THOUGHT OF THAT BEFORE YOU BROUGHT THEM OUT HERE.

YEAH, THANKS FOR THE WISE COUNSEL.

I TAKE IT YOU HAVEN'T TOLD HER YET?

NO, OF COURSE NOT.

ONE DAY WHEN I WAS TEN YEARS OLD, MY LIFE CHANGED FOREVER.

ELIZABETH CAUGHT ME TRYING TO STEAL A COIN PURSE OFF HER BELT.

SNATCH

I THOUGHT FOR SURE SHE WAS GOING TO KILL ME.

BUT WHEN SHE SAW ME, HER FACE JUST TURNED TO COMPASSION.

THE CAPTAIN'S GONE SOFT--SHE WANTS OUT OF THE GAME. WE ALL SAW IT COMING.

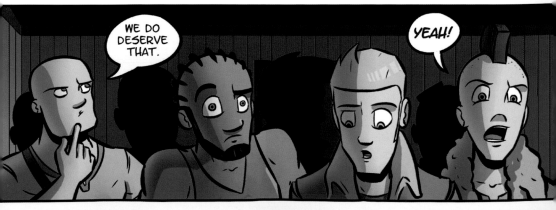

YOU KNOW WE COULD JUST TAKE THE CROWN AND--

FINE.

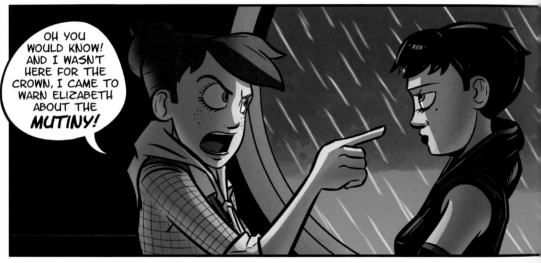

BLAM!

BLAM!

BLAM!

SLAM!

WHAM!

WHERE DID THEY GO?

TEAR THIS PLACE APART! FIND THEM!

DO YOU ALWAYS SLEEP WITH YOUR BOOTS ON?

WHEN YOU HAVE AS MANY ENEMIES AS ME, YOU DO.

YOU MEAN YOUR CHARMING PERSONALITY HASN'T WON YOU MANY FRIENDS?

FUNNY.

MUST GET TIRED OF LOOKING OVER YOUR SHOULDER ALL THE TIME.

YOU HAVE NO IDEA.

WOAH! **WOAH!** LET'S TALK ABOUT THIS!

WHAM

NICE MOVES, KID! WHERE DID YOU LEARN TO HANDLE A SWORD LIKE THAT?

FIVE YEARS OF FENCING. STATE CHAMP TWO YEARS IN A ROW.

WHAT ARE YOU DOING? GET BACK IN THE PLANE!

EVENIN' CAPTAIN.

YOU DON'T WANT TO MAKE THIS DIFFICULT, READ.

I PROMISE.

NOW TOSS IT AT MY FEET, NICE AND EASY.

WINCH RELEAS

THUNK

CRA-KANK!

WARNING

JACKIE! CUT THE CHAIN!

CREEK!

WHAT ARE YOU--?

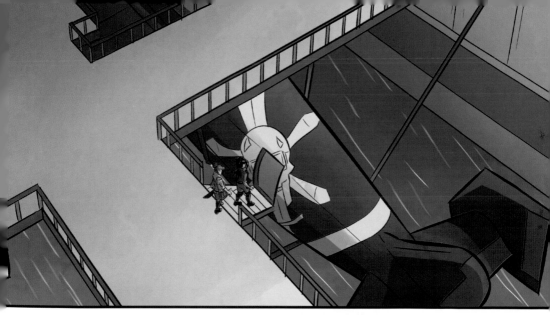

TELL ME THE TRUTH, WHY DO YOU REALLY WANT THE CROWN?

WHY DO YOU CARE?

BECAUSE I'M CURIOU-- *GASP!*

WHAT?

SPECIAL THANKS

To my savior, Jesus Christ, who has given me everything. To my parents who have always supported me and always backed me up. I would not have gotten this far without their support and wisdom. To my friends and critique circle, Michael Regina, Stephen McCranie, Jonny Jimison, and Will Terrel, who helped me shape this book into what it is today. To the friends who helped me proof read and edit the book, Shane Houghton, Jonny Jimision, and David R. Krigbaum.

THANKS TO KICKSTARTER BACKERS

A special thanks to everyone who supported the Kickstarter campaign which allowed this book to see print, and an extra special thanks to the following people who rose above and beyond in their donations to make sure the campaign was a success.

Scott P. McClellan

Charlie and Lacy Dyer

Bob and Rose Schaetzl

Jason Freund

Christine Anderson

Cédric Barthels

David V Gresham

David R. Krigbaum

Scott Miyamoto

Benjamin Archer and Nick Zajdel

Scott Early

Michael Canavan

Shellie Patterson

Ed R

Henrik Lindhe

Foli Ayivoh

John M. Phillips